i-SPY

my first wildlife

SPY IT! STICK IT!

Published by **Collins** An imprint of HarperCollins Publishers
Westerhill Road, Bishopbriggs, Glasgow G64 2QT
www.harpercollins.co.uk

HarperCollins Publishers
1st Floor, Watermarque Building, Ringsend Road, Dublin 4, Ireland

Publisher: Michelle I'Anson
Head of Creative Services: Craig Balfour
Designer: Kevin Robbins
Layout: Jouve
Editorial: Jill Laidlaw, Lauren Reid, Carol Medcalf

 A catalogue record for this book is available from the British Library.

ISBN 9780008529802

Printed in Europe

10 9 8 7 6 5 4 3 2 1

Acknowledgements
Images used under license
from Shutterstock.com.

How to use your i-SPY book

Look out for the things in the book.

If you spy it, put a sticker in the circle.

Keep your eyes peeled for Top Spots. These are hard to find, so you'll have to search high and low to see them.

Ask a grown up to help you add up your points. When you score 100 points, you get your super spotter sticker!

Grey squirrel

1 point

Hedgehog

TOP SPOT!

3 points

SUPER SPOTTER

Note to grown up

Send in for your FREE i-SPY progress poster, where your child can stick their super-spotter stickers!

Head to collins.co.uk/i-SPY for details

In the garden

You don't need to go far to spot these creatures. Take a look outside where you live to see what you can find.

Grey squirrel

STICK IT!

1 point

Foxes live in underground dens.

Daisy

STICK IT!

1 point

Fox

STICK IT!

2 points

Hedgehog

TOP SPOT!

3 points

Baby hedgehogs are called hoglets.

Bumblebee

STICK IT!

1 point

Earthworm

STICK IT!

1 point

Garden snail

STICK IT!

1 point

Wasp

STICK IT!

1 point

Mice can squeeze through tiny gaps.

House mouse

TOP SPOT!

3 points

You can attract birds to your garden or windowsill by putting out feed and fresh water.

Female blackbirds are brown, not black.

Starling

STICK IT!

1 point

Blackbird

STICK IT!

1 point

Robin

STICK IT!

1 point

Rose

STICK IT!

2 points

Collared dove

STICK IT!

1 point

Wren

TOP SPOT!

3 points

House sparrow

STICK IT!

2 points

Goldfinch

STICK IT!

2 point

A flock of goldfinches is called a charm.

At the pond

Amphibians are animals that live both in water and on land. In and around ponds are a great place to spot them.

Frog spaw

STICK IT!

2 points

Frogs drink water through their skin.

Newt

TOP SPOT!

3 points

Frog

STICK IT!

1 point

Hornwort

STICK IT!

1 point

Tadpoles

TOP SPOT!

3 points

Water lily

STICK IT!

2 points

Toad

STICK IT!

2 points

Don't just search in the water for creatures. Look in the air and in the plants nearby.

Water beetle

STICK IT!

1 point

Pond-skater

STICK IT!

1 point

Water boatman

STICK IT!

1 point

Water snail

STICK IT!

1 point

Water snails do not have ears.

Dragonfly

TOP SPOT!

3 points

Leeches have 32 brains.

Leech

STICK IT!

2 points

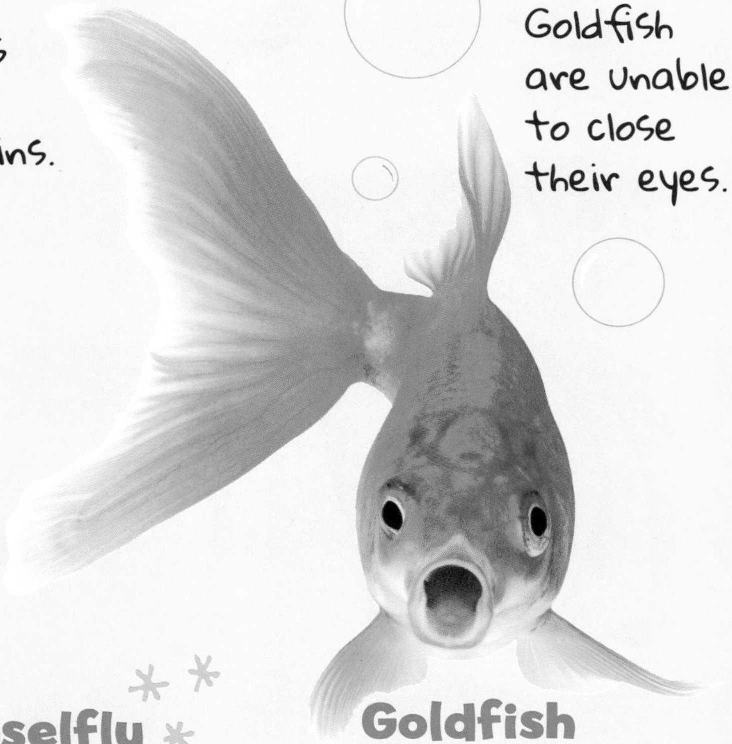

Goldfish are unable to close their eyes.

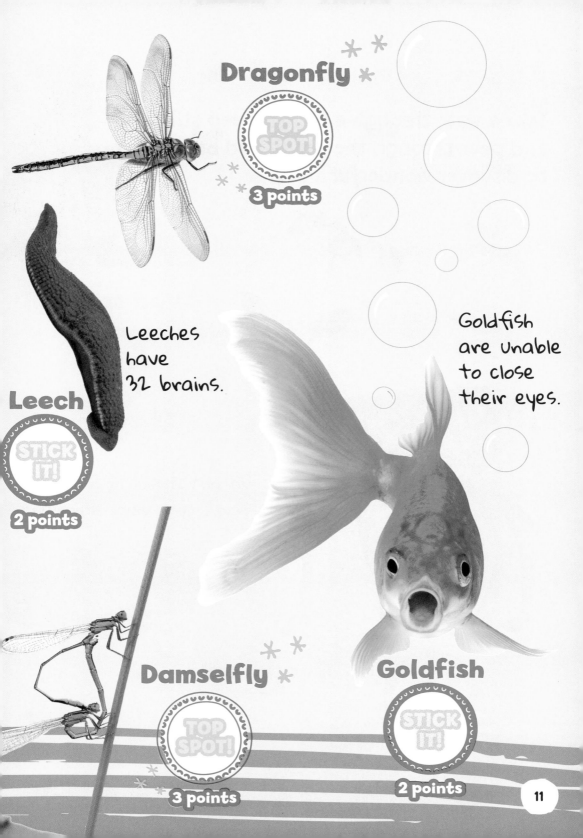

Damselfly

TOP SPOT!

3 points

Goldfish

STICK IT!

2 points

In the forest

Take a walk through a forest. Keep still and peer through the leaves and branches to discover wonderful animals.

Ant

STICK IT!

1 point

Red squirrel

STICK IT!

2 points

Do not touch fungi! Some are very dangerous.

Deer

STICK IT!

2 points

Toadstool

TOP SPOT!

3 points

Pine marten

TOP SPOT!

3 points

Bat

TOP SPOT!

3 points

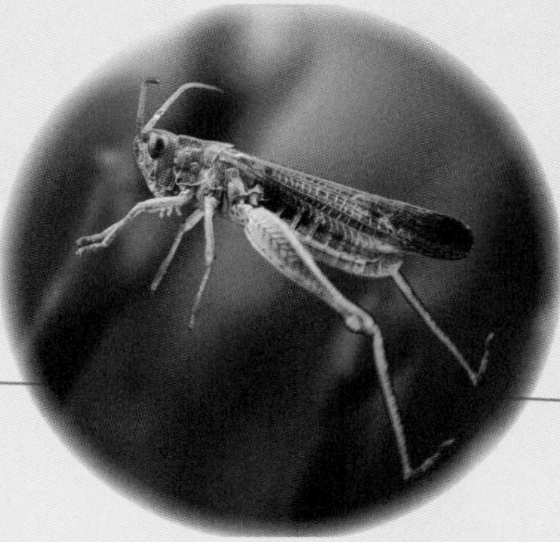

Grasshopper

STICK IT!

2 points

Badgers use their poo to mark territory.

Badger

TOP SPOT!

3 points

These animals live in the forest. They can be hard to spot in the wild but you may also find them in a zoo or wildlife park.

Caterpillar

STICK IT!

2 points

Wood mouse

STICK IT!

2 points

Cuckoos lay their eggs in other birds' nests.

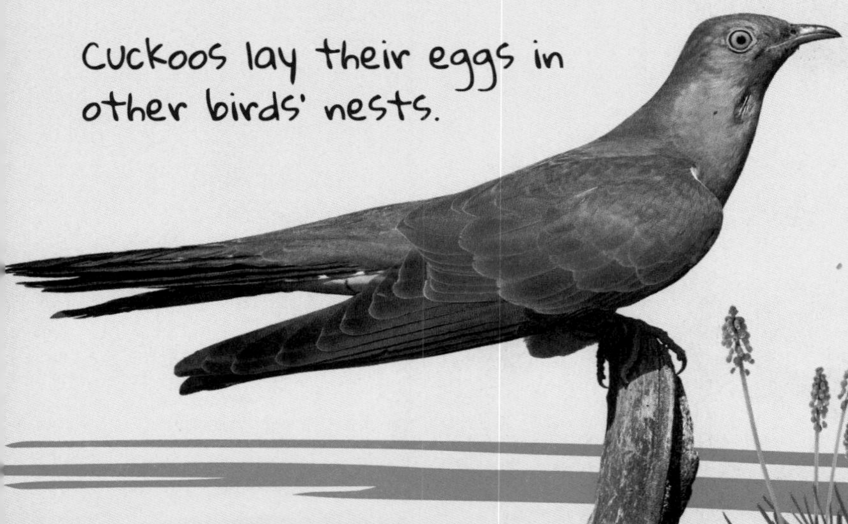

Cuckoo

TOP SPOT!

3 points

Barn owl

STICK IT!

2 points

Barn owls are silent when they fly.

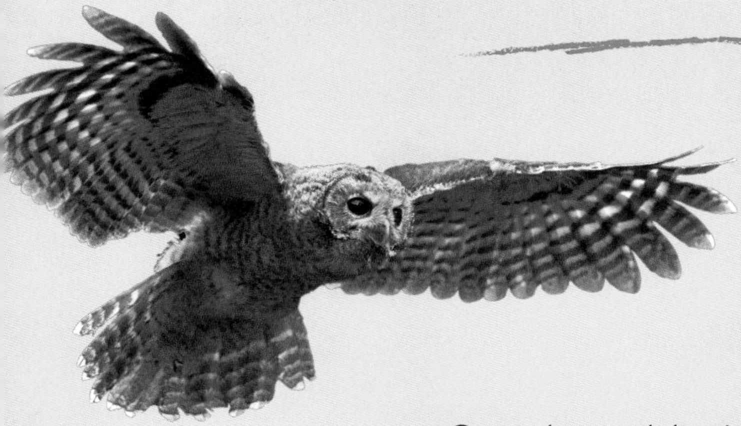

Tawny owl

TOP SPOT!

3 points

Great spotted woodpeckers nest in holes in trees.

Bluebells

STICK IT!

2 points

Great spotted woodpecker

STICK IT!

2 points

At the river

Be careful as you spy animals next to the river. Rivers can be fast flowing and deep.

River otters can hold their breath for up to 8 minutes.

Otter

2 points

Water vole

3 points

Beaver

3 points

Beavers have large, flat tails that help them when swimming.

American mink

TOP SPOT!

3 points

Reeds

STICK IT!

1 point

Water shrew

STICK IT!

2 points

Polecat

TOP SPOT!

3 points

River animals have special body parts to help them move through water such as webbed feet or fins.

Salmon can leap high out of rivers.

A baby swan is called a 'cygnet'.

Salmon

TOP SPOT!

3 points

Swan

STICK IT!

1 point

Trout

STICK IT!

2 points

Heron

STICK IT!

2 points

Cormorant

TOP SPOT!

3 points

Carp

STICK IT!

1 point

Duck

STICK IT!

1 point

Kingfisher

TOP SPOT!

3 points

Kingfishers close their eyes when they dive into water.

In the country

Many types of wildlife can be found in the countryside. There is lots of food and shelter there.

Little owl

TOP SPOT!

3 points

Adder

TOP SPOT!

3 points

Harvest mouse

TOP SPOT!

3 points

Snowdrops

STICK IT!

1 point

Shield bug

STICK IT!

2 points

Brown rat

STICK IT!

2 points

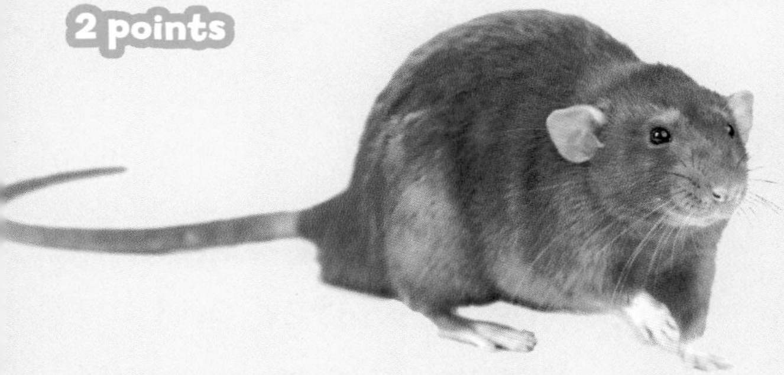

Rabbit

STICK IT!

1 point

Rabbits' teeth never stop growing.

Walking in the country is a a fun activity. Next time you are on a country walk see what wildlife you can spot.

Crows have excellent memories.

Crow

STICK IT!

1 point

Stoat

TOP SPOT!

3 points

Stoats have white fur in winter and brown fur in summer.

Butterfly

STICK IT!

1 point

Mole

TOP SPOT!

3 points

Moles have curved paws and claws for digging.

Spider

STICK IT!

1 point

Dog rose

STICK IT!

2 points

rass snake

STICK IT!

2 points

In the mountains and on the moors

Mountains and moors are open areas of land that are filled with wildlife.

Mountain hare

STICK IT!

2 points

Stag

STICK IT!

1 point

Feral goat

STICK IT!

2 points

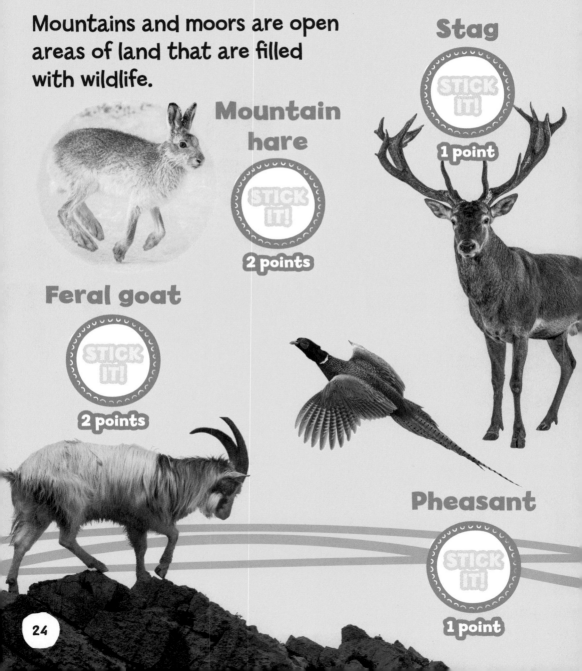

Pheasant

STICK IT!

1 point

Heather

STICK IT!

1 point

Highland cow

Highland cows have very shaggy hair.

STICK IT!

2 points

Scottish wildcats are also known as 'Highland tigers'.

Scottish wildcat

TOP SPOT!

3 points

Look above when you are in the moors or mountains; you may see birds of prey high in the sky searching for food. You may also find these birds at wildlife centres.

Red kite

TOP SPOT!

3 points

Peregrine falcons can move faster than any other animal.

Sparrowhawk

STICK IT!

2 points

Peregrine falcon

STICK IT!

2 points

Red grouse

TOP SPOT!

3 points

Golden eagle

TOP SPOT!

3 points

Eagles and kestrels are birds of prey.

Kestrel

STICK IT!

1 point

Capercaillie

TOP SPOT!

3 points

At the coast

When you next go to the beach, look for wildlife in the sand, out at sea and in rock pools.

Sea urchin

STICK IT!

1 point

Sea urchins have five teeth.

Bottleno dolphi

STICK IT!

2 points

Grey se

STICK IT!

1 point

Jellyfish

STICK IT!

1 point

Jellyfish can be found in every ocean.

Lobster

STICK IT!

2 points

Starfish

STICK IT!

2 points

Crabs have 10 legs.

Crab

STICK IT!

1 point

Seaweed

STICK IT!

1 point

Many birds live near the sea. They nest in sea cliffs and hunt for food in the water below.

Gannet

TOP SPOT!

3 points

Gannets are the biggest sea birds in Britain.

Common tern

STICK IT!

1 point

Puffins are nicknamed 'sea parrots'.

Puffin

STICK IT!

2 points

Seagull

STICK IT!

1 point

Oystercatcher

STICK IT!

2 points

Avocet

STICK IT!

2 points

Sandpiper

STICK IT!

1 point

What else can you spot?

Get little ones started on their very own spotting adventure with My First i-SPY sticker books! Packed with fun facts and photographs to keep children entertained. To see the full collection, go to collins.co.uk/i-spy